Illustrated by Tony Blundell

Scholastic Children's Books,
Commonwealth House, 1-19 New Oxford Street,
London WC1A 1NU, UK

A division of Scholastic Ltd
London ~ New York ~ Toronto ~ Sydney ~ Auckland

First published in the UK by Scholastic Ltd, 1993
This edition published by Scholastic Ltd, 1997

ISBN 0 590 13661 5

Printed by Cox & Wyman Ltd, Reading, Berks

10 9 8 7 6 5 4 3 2 1

CONGRATULATIONS

You have in your hands the key to one of the most dreadful and dangerous weapons EVER!

Imagine the POWER! Teachers will tremble, bullies will buckle and parents will panic, because YOU can threaten them with . . .

THE DEADLIEST JOKE IN THE UNIVERSE!

HOW CAN A JOKE BE DEADLY?

As you know, some jokes are REALLY funny and everybody laughs a lot.

Some jokes are only MEDIUMLY funny, and people only smile a bit.

Then there are some jokes that are *so* BAD, that people groan.

There are even some jokes that are so TERRIBLE that people feel ill, and they ask you to stop telling any more jokes.

Then there are one or two jokes that are *so* SCREAMINGLY WRETCHED that people positively BEG you not to tell them!

BUT NOW! There is ONE joke that is so MIND-DESTROYINGLY CATASTROPHIC that it is . . .

THE DEADLIEST JOKE IN THE UNIVERSE

Of course, if this joke was simply written out so that everybody could read it, then people everywhere would be falling down, screaming, running away, or flying off into outer space to find a new place to live. Therefore, the DEADLIEST JOKE has been put into code.

This book contains the code. If you can break it, then you could have control of

HOW TO FIND THE DEADLIEST JOKE

Nearly every page in this book has three things on it. It has:

the first part of a joke at the top

a puzzle in the middle

the punchline to another joke at the bottom

Look! There's even the punchline to a joke at the bottom of this page!

 ☐ *Nun*

WHAT YOU DO

1 Read the first part of the joke.
2 Solve the puzzle, and that will give you a number. This number refers to the page with the answer to the joke.

3 Turn to the answer at the bottom of the page. If you got the puzzle right, then the answer will be FUNNY and you can have a big laugh.
4 Next to the answer is a little box. PUT A TICK IN THE BOX!

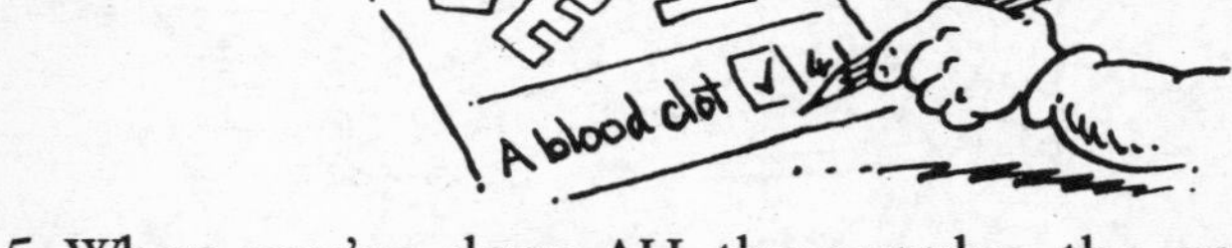

5 When you've done ALL the puzzles, the end of the book tells you what to do next.

If you see this sign by a puzzle, that means somewhere else in the book there is a hint . . . if you need it. And you quite probably will, because, this code is SO deadly, we can't possibly print any answers!

Of course, you need to learn the DEADLIEST JOKE before anybody else does, so turn the page QUICKLY and get started!

What's MAD and goes to the MOON?

Here's a man who'd like to be mad and go to the moon.

Professor Stan Backabit

He is the inventor of many great items including the Edible Dog Lead, the SQUARE Football, Upsidedown Trees, Three-sided Paper and, of course, his Amazing Disappearing

Here is his SECRET CODE

NUMBER machine!

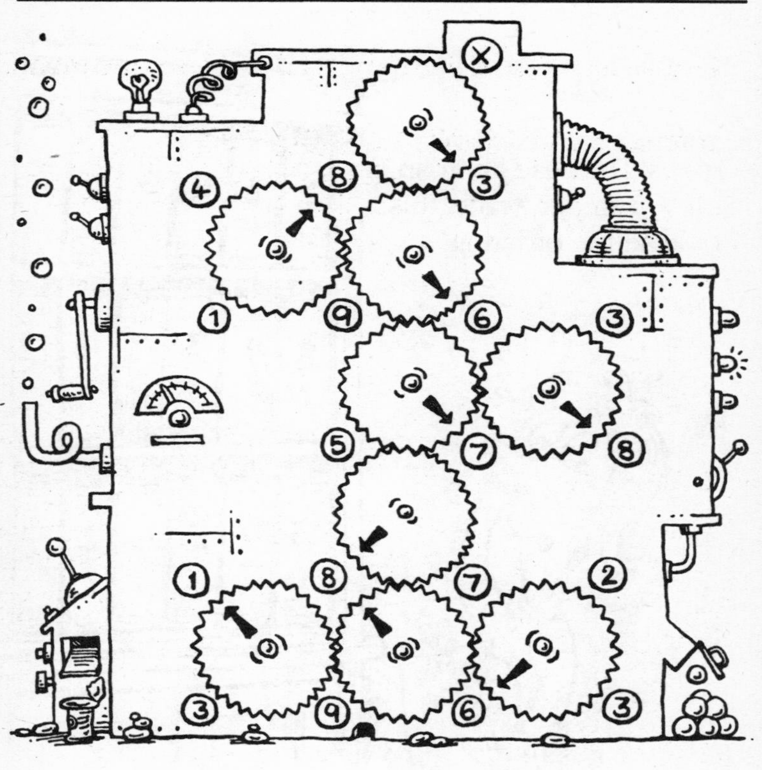

If the cog wheel at the top moves a quarter turn, so that the arrow points at the "X", you'll see all the other wheels move a quarter turn, too.

Mark where all the other arrows move to. Add up the numbers they point at!

They're always in their bare skins. ☐

Where would you find a dead BOOKWORM*?*

Ooops! The head librarian, Phil V. Temper, wants this bookshelf re-ordering!

Add together the numbers of all the books that are in the wrong place.
Subtract the number of the missing book.

 ☐ *You were built upside down.*

Why don't you ever get HUNGRY *on the beach?*

Add up the pairs of pincers on the crabs, multiply them by the legs on the starfish, then subtract the wings on the seagulls.

Two fish swimming backwards. ☐

What's the most PAINFUL CAKE?

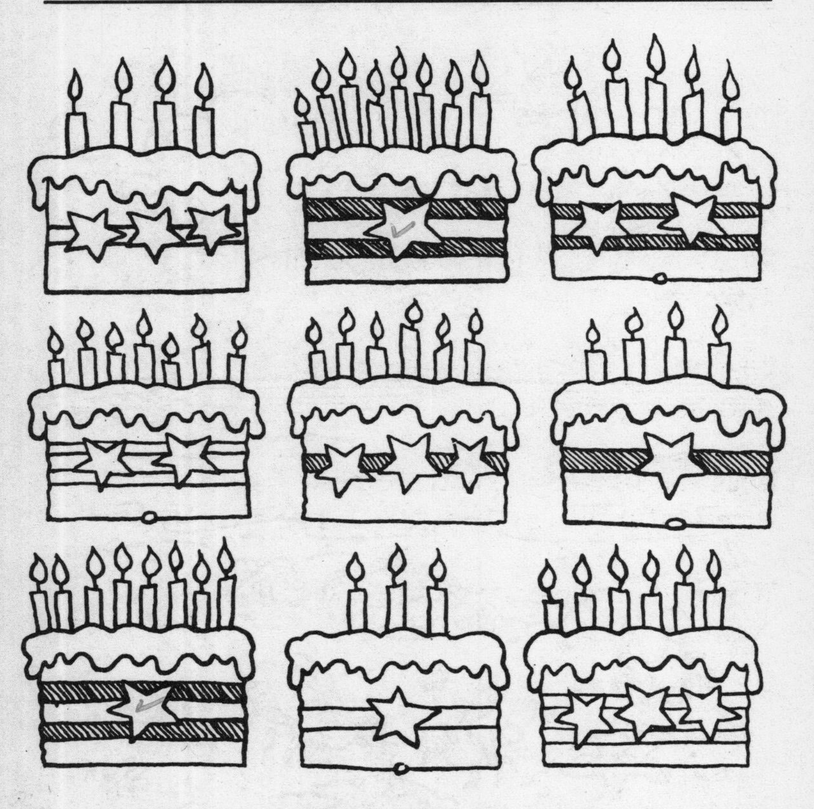

Apart from the candles, only two of these cakes are identical!

What is the total number of candles on the two identical cakes?

Her coach was a pumpkin.

Here are some extra silly jokes:

What's the best thing to put into a cake?
Your teeth.

What kind of cake disappears?
A scone (s'gone!).

What sort of cake shouldn't you eat?
A cake of soap.

What sort of cake can you use in the shower?
A sponge cake.

It is night-time in the offices of Grimm Ltd.

As usual, ALL the lights have been left on.

The row of windows going up the middle of the building is the lift shaft.

The security man, Al Avvalluk, does not bother with the top floor, but he takes the lift to the next one down. He turns left out of the lift and switches off the lights in the first two rooms.

He then takes the lift down two more floors and again turns left but only switches off the lights in the two furthest rooms.

He then decides to have a cup of tea, so he goes to the kitchen, which is back along the corridor, the second door after the lift. He plugs in the kettle, which fuses the kitchen light and also fuses the light of the room two floors above.

In confusion, he dashes back to the lift, goes down and then turns all the lift lights out.

Shade in the windows where the lights go out!

Then look for the answer in the lighted windows.

A dead kangaroo. ☐

What happened to the cat in the MILK DRINKING *race?*

Old Mrs Littertray had 2 cats.

Each cat had three kittens.

Each kitten grew up and had two more kittens.

How many legs were there in Mrs Littertray's house?

(She didn't have any chairs or tables or pianos!)

 ☐ *A stomach-ache.*

Who made ROBIN HOOD'S *chips?*

The famous, if erratic, archer, Sheila Vuriyout was practising.

She fired three arrows at this target. Each scored a different amount.

Her first arrow scored five times more than one of the others.
Her second arrow scored least.
Her third arrow scored half of one of the others.

What was her total score? 40 ?

Here are two of the silliest dice in the world!

Let's throw them and see what we get . . .

. . . there!

Now we'll throw them once more . . .

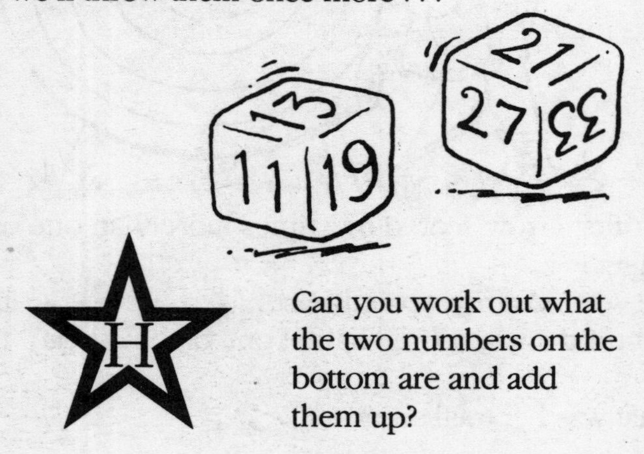

Can you work out what the two numbers on the bottom are and add them up?

What's a CALENDAR'S favourite food?

How much do you know about time? Try this simple sum.

The number of SECONDS in a minute? [ ]
minus the number of HOURS in a day −[ ]
=[ ]
times the number of MONTHS in a year x[ ]
=[ ]
minus the number of DAYS in a year −[ ]
=[ ]
plus the number of WEEKS in a year +[ ]
=[ ]
divided by the number of DAYS in a week÷[ ]
=[ ]
plus the number of MINUTES in an hour +[ ]

makes . . . = [ ]

It will fall off the shelf. ☐

What do you call an invention for seeing through SOLID brick walls?

Here's a solid brick wall with a snail on it.
The snail is trying to reach the flower by following the directions on the bricks. You'll see the first brick he's on is labelled D2. This means he has to slither DOWN two bricks. The brick he lands on says R3, so he then goes RIGHT for three bricks. L means LEFT and you'll just have to guess what U means!

Wherever he goes, the snail leaves his slimy trail. When he finally reaches the flower, how many bricks have slime on them?

D2	D5	R1	D3	L3
R2	R2	D7	D3	D7
R3	L1	D3	D5	L3
U3	R3	L2	L1	L3
R4	U4	D2	U3	L3
D2	L1	D3	R1	U5
D2	D3	R2	L2	D3
U6	R2	L2	U1	U3
R3	U2	U4	U5	L1
U1	R2	R2	U4	

It gives a little wave. ☐

Where did GRIM JIM the Pirate keep his BUCCANEERS?

GRIM JIM the pirate buried his treasure all over the island shown on this map. The exact position of each treasure is marked with an "X".

Recently, two sailors, Mandy Lifeboats and Ray Zuddeanker, arrived on the island and started finding the treasures.

GRIM JIM had indicated where each treasure was with this set of code numbers:

Each treasure's code number was made by using the map reference numbers and multiplying them together. For instance the map reference of the GOLD was 5/9. (They went along to number 5 then moved up to number 9). The code number for the GOLD was 5×9=45.

One code number was added as a booby trap . . . but which one?

☐ *Because he got the sack.*

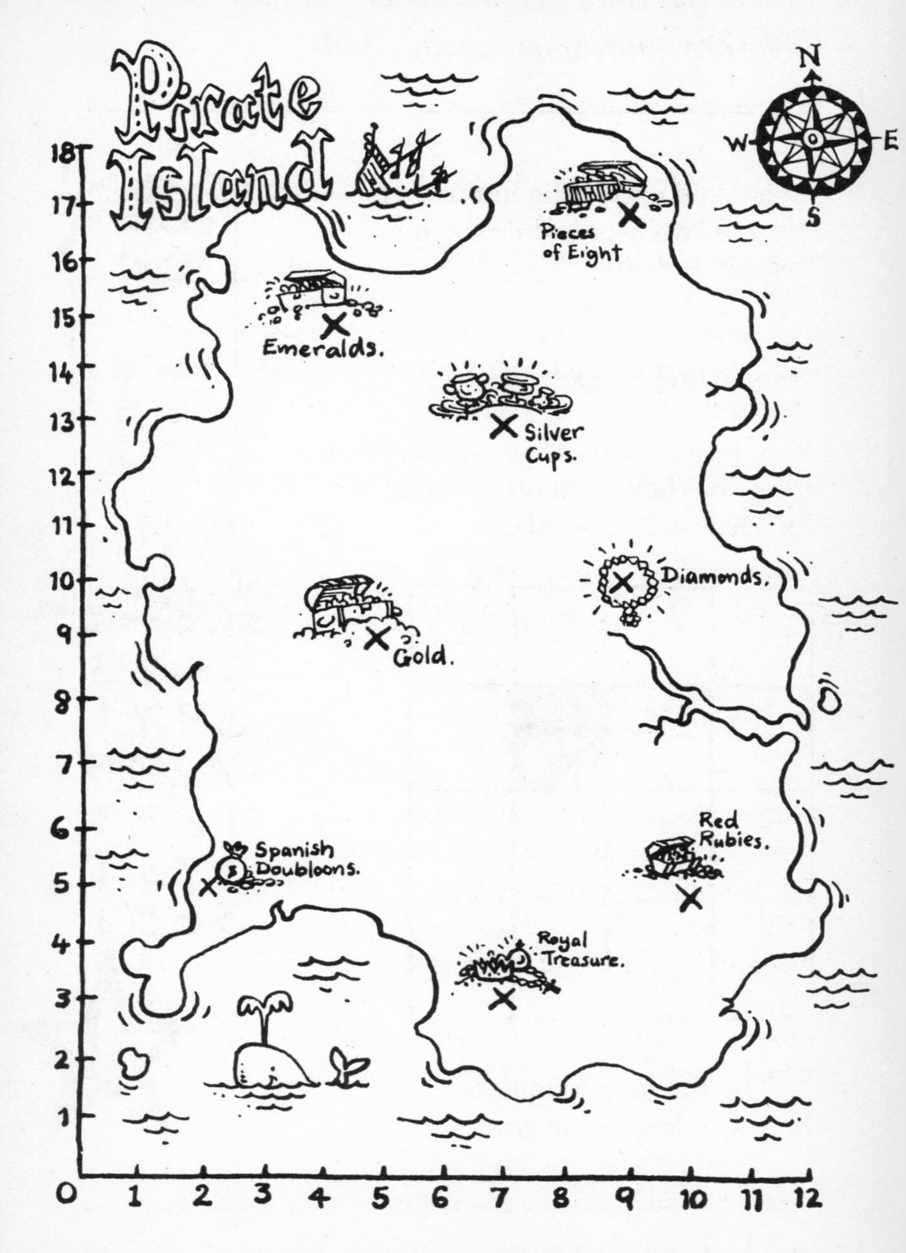
Pirate Island
N
W
E
S
Pieces of Eight
Emeralds.
Silver Cups.
Diamonds.
Gold.
Red Rubies.
Spanish Doubloons.
Royal Treasure.
18
17
16
15
14
13
12
11
10
9
8
7
6
5
4
3
2
1
0
1
2
3
4
5
6
7
8
9
10
11
12

Why are guardsmen always cold?

Guards do everything in numbers — even in crosswords they use numbers instead of words.

Try this one for example:

You have to fit these six numbers into the grid. They go in up or down, forwards or backwards.

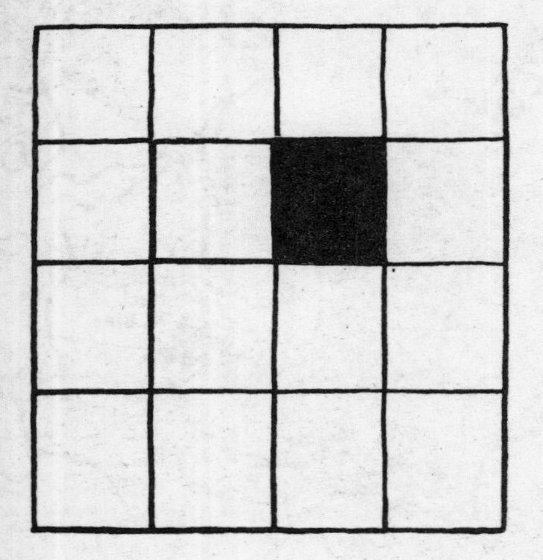

7423
3971
7235
1831
1741
3651

Add up the three numbers in the middle of the grid.

 ☐ *She wanted to get on the bus.*

Why should you never buy a violin at a car boot sale?

Three friends each bought a toy at a car boot sale. Together they spent £1.80.

Alice spent less than Cathy, who bought the paint set.

The doll cost 20p more than the ball.

The cheapest toy was 50p.

How much did Brenda spend?

Three little elephants. ☐

Why is a leg always upside down?

There are some pretty strange-looking monsters living far away on Planet Plimsole. It's lucky that the planet is far away because the monsters all have lots of feet and toes, making it the smelliest place in the Universe.

However, the monsters are very proud of their smelly feet, and each monster's importance is measured by his smell rating. A monster's rating is calculated by multiplying his feet by his toes.

Here you can see some monsters' feet. The least important monster has a smell rating of just ten.

What is the most important monster's rating?

 ☐ *An octobus.*

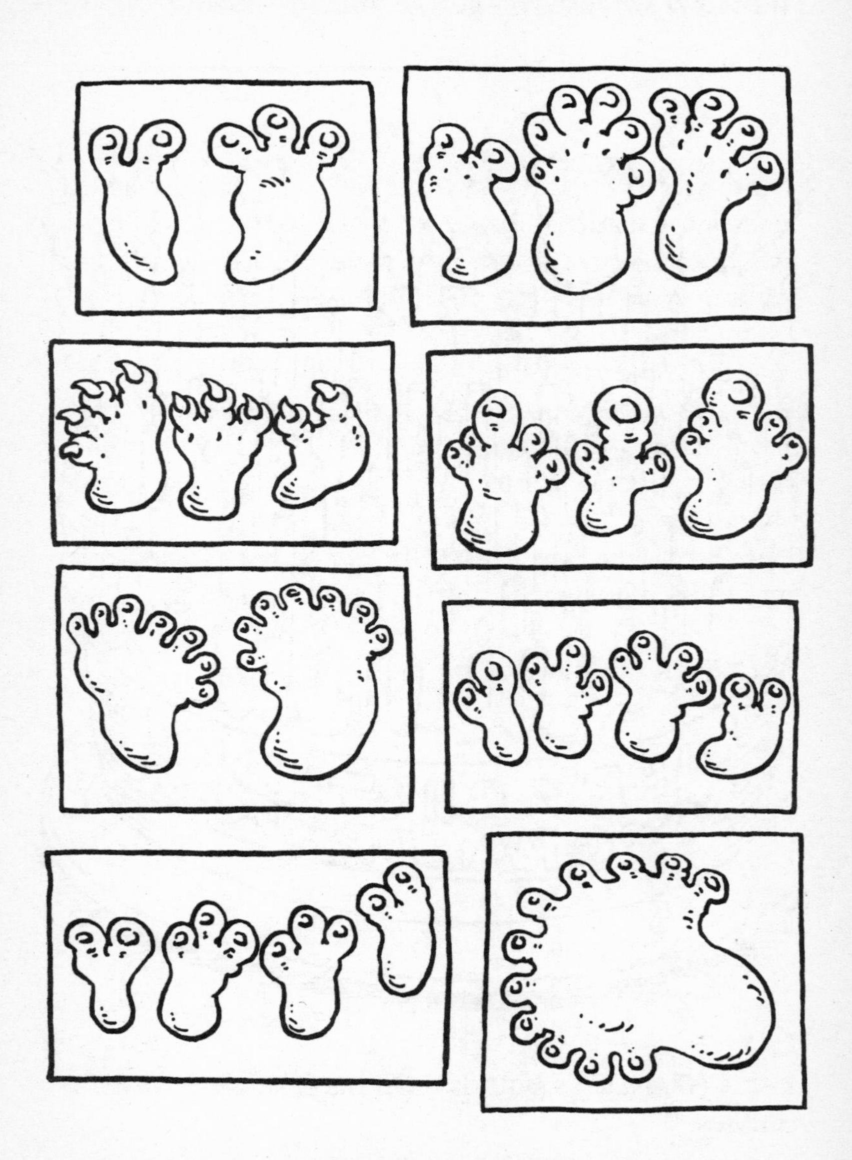

What do you always get on your birthday?

It was GRANDPA's Birthday. On his cake were NINETY candles!

First GRANDPA himself blew some candles out.

Then UNCLE FRED blew out exactly half the candles left alight.

Next AUNTIE DOREEN blew out six candles.

After AUNTIE DOREEN, COUSIN RODNEY blew out exactly half the number of candles that GRANDPA had originally blown out.

Finally GRANDPA had another go. This time he blew out exactly half the number that UNCLE FRED had blown out.

After all that, three candles were *still* burning.

How many candles did FRED blow out?

It saw the cowslip. ☐

What takes eight people for trips around the ocean?

One of the most unexciting toys of all time is the "Middle of the ocean Jigsaw Puzzle." It consists of twenty-seven thousand pieces, all of which look exactly the same. (They're all blue.)

After ninety-seven years locked in a darkened turret, Auntie Social is about to complete the puzzle, at last. There are just six empty places left in the middle, of the puzzle, as you can see from the picture.

 ☐ *It's too weak.*

UNFORTUNATELY . . . Auntie Social has seven pieces left!

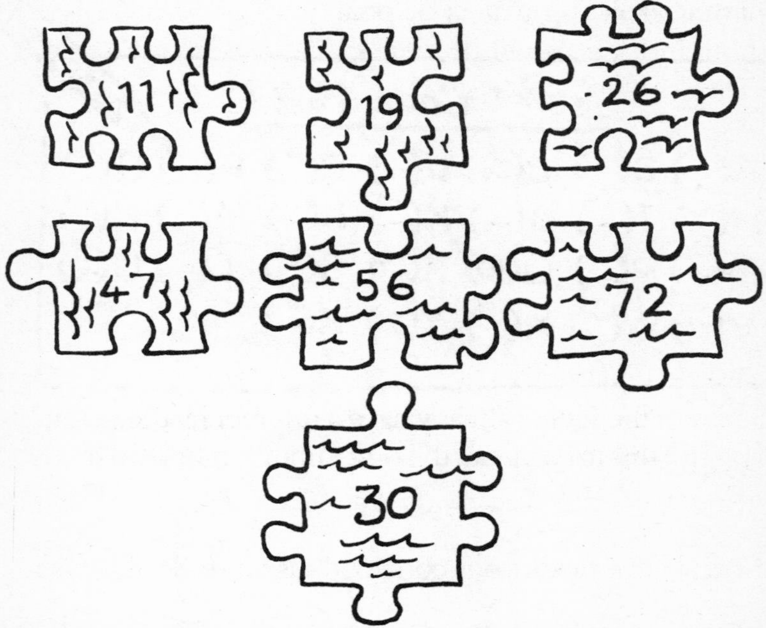

Here are the seven pieces, each with a reference number. Which piece doesn't she need?

What's green and sends secret messages?

Here's a nice simple secret message for you, but first you have to make up your code pad!

Secret Code Pad!

A( ) B( ) C(24) D( ) E( ) F( ) G( )
H( ) I( ) J( ) K( ) L( ) M( ) N( )
O( ) P( ) Q(10) R( ) S( ) T( ) U( )
V( ) W( ) X( ) Y(2) Z( )

Some of the letters already have a number by them. Can you use this to work out the other numbers and fill them in?

Now you've made your code pad, use it to decode this message:

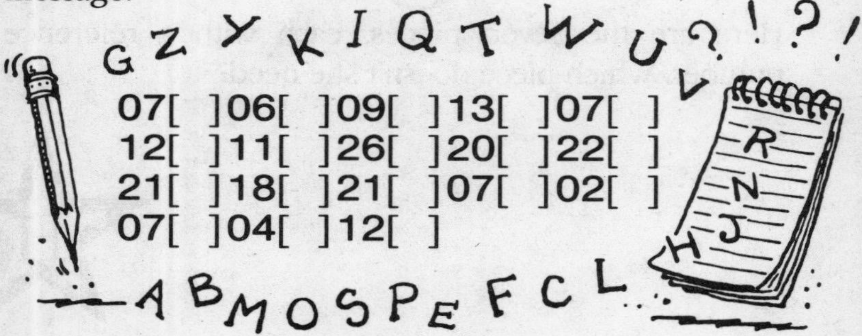

Here are some extra messages to decode!

This may help you to fill in the number crossword on page 24.

07[ ]19[ ]22[ ]07[ ]12[ ]
11[ ]15[ ]18[ ]13[ ]22[ ]
18[ ]08[ ]12[ ]13[ ]22[ ]
08[ ]22[ ]05[ ]22[ ]13[ ]
13[ ]18[ ]13[ ]22[ ]07[ ]
19[ ]09[ ]22[ ]22[ ]

Here's a hint for Grandpa's candles on page 28.

20[ ] 9[ ] 26[ ] 13[ ] 23[ ] 11[ ]
26[ ] 25[ ] 15[ ] 12[ ] 4[ ] 8[ ]
12[ ] 6[ ] 7[ ] 13[ ] 22[ ] 26[ ]
9[ ] 15[ ] 2[ ] 7[ ] 4[ ] 22[ ]
13[ ] 7[ ] 2[ ] 22[ ] 26[ ] 24[ ]
19[ ] 7[ ] 18[ ] 14[ ] 22[ ]

And here's a clue about Mrs Littertray's cats on page 16.

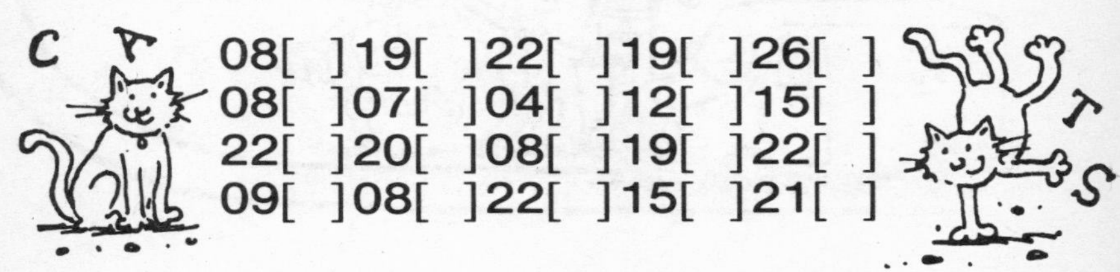

08[ ]19[ ]22[ ]19[ ]26[ ]
08[ ]07[ ]04[ ]12[ ]15[ ]
22[ ]20[ ]08[ ]19[ ]22[ ]
09[ ]08[ ]22[ ]15[ ]21[ ]

Why was the POSTMAN crying?

Nora Notheryear is having a birthday party.

Her boyfriend Luke Everywhere has finally found the estate she lives on, but has has to ask directions from Bill Bringer the postman.

Here's what Bill said . . .

Go to the roundabout, take the third exit, go past five houses and turn left, then go round the next left hand corner too, then take your second right and right again at the T junction, go down and take the third right, then follow the road round until you get to the roundabout, go straight over then first left, round the corner, then first left, second right, follow the road round, then there's a left turning but go past that and it's the second house on your left.

What number is Nora's house?

 ☐ *It was a little pail.*

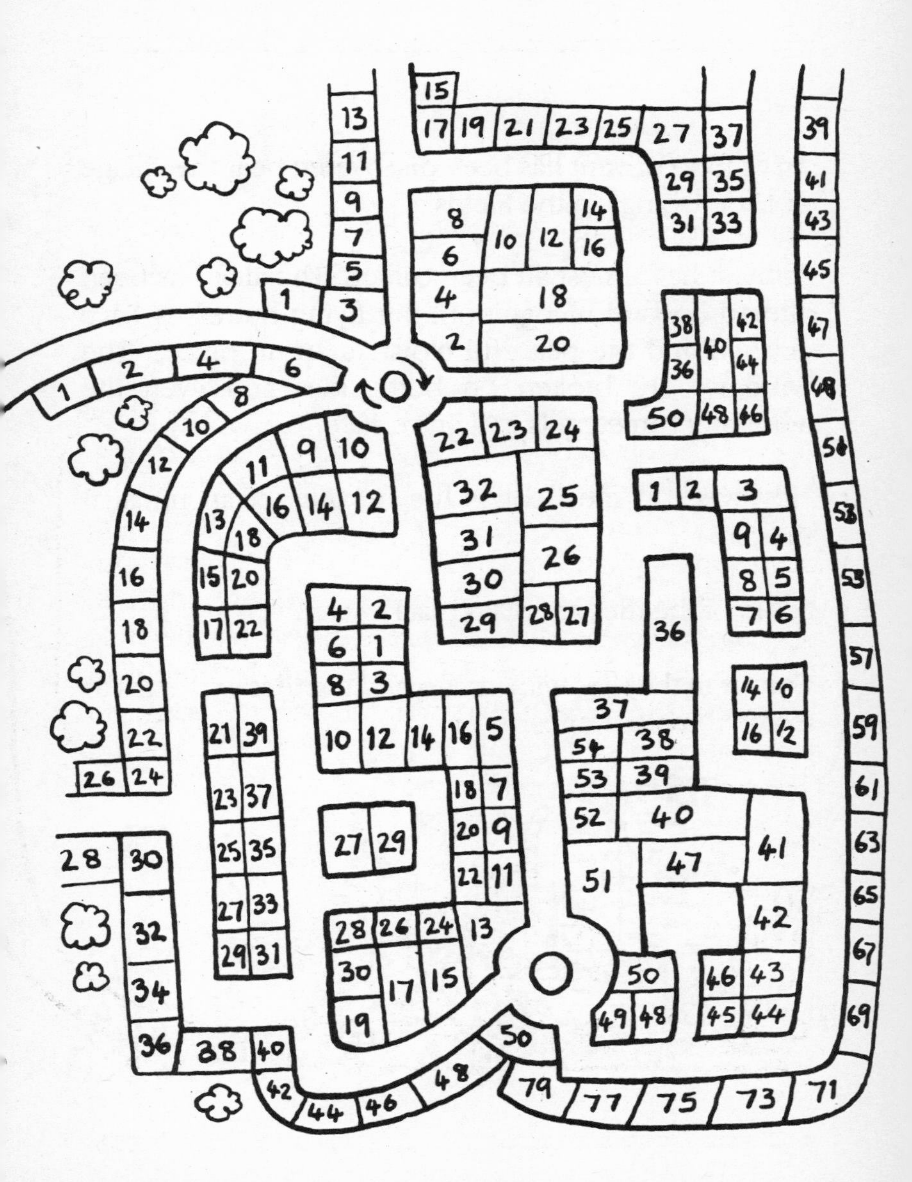
15
13
17 19 21 23 25 27 37
39
11
29 35
41
9
8
14
31 33
43
7
10 12
16
6
5
45
1
3
4
18
38
42
47
40
2
20
36
44
1
2
4
6
8
50 48 46
49
10
22 23 24
9
10
12
11
32
25
1 2 3
51
16 14 12
13
14
18
9 4
31
26
15 20
4 2
30
8 5
16
53
28 27
17 22
29
7 6
36
18
6 1
57
8 3
14 10
37
20
21 39
10 12 14 16 5
54 38
59
22
16 12
53 39
26 24
18 7
23 37
61
52
40
20 9
27 29
28 30
63
25 35
41
22 11
47
51
65
27 33
42
32
28 26 24 13
67
29 31
30
43
17 15
46
34
50
69
49 48
45 44
19
36
38 40
50
42
48
79
71
73
75
77
44 46

What sort of people do you find in an empty convent?

An empty convent has been discovered near the village of Little Doings in the Fields.

Sadly, it has almost all been ruined. The altar has been altered beyond recognition, the flying butresses have crashed and the peaceful cloisters are in pieces. The windows are broken on both sides and even the adjoining cemetery is in a grave state.

However, on the floor is the remains of an unusual mosaic.

Some of the tiles are plain black.

Colour in the tiles with circles and the tiles with stars to match the black ones.

 ☐ *A year older.*

Can you see the hidden number?
Try turning the book around if you can't.

Why was Cinderella lousy at football?

Here's Cinderella arriving at the ball! Look at the clock – it's a miniature of Big Ben, with four faces!

 ☐ *One sentence can take years.*

Now It's gone midnight. When Cinderella dashed away, she knocked the clock over! Every single number has fallen off!

Some numbers have gone missing. What do they add up to?

What do you call two spiders on honeymoon?

Creepy the Spider is going to visit his girlfriend. He is a bit of a creep too – he's always saying "What a nice pair of legs pair of legs pair of legs," to her.

As he's promised to pick up some dinner on the way, Creepy is going to collect as many of the flies stuck on the web as he can.

 ☐ *A bird in a submarine.*

In order not to wear the web out, Creepy may not walk along any strand more than once, and he may not double back.

He finds he can get all the flies but one! What number is it?

Why did the teacher go to the optician?

Oh dear! The bossy teacher, Sid Owanshuddup, has set a problem that somebody obviously couldn't be bothered with. It has been torn out of an exercise book and cut into pieces!

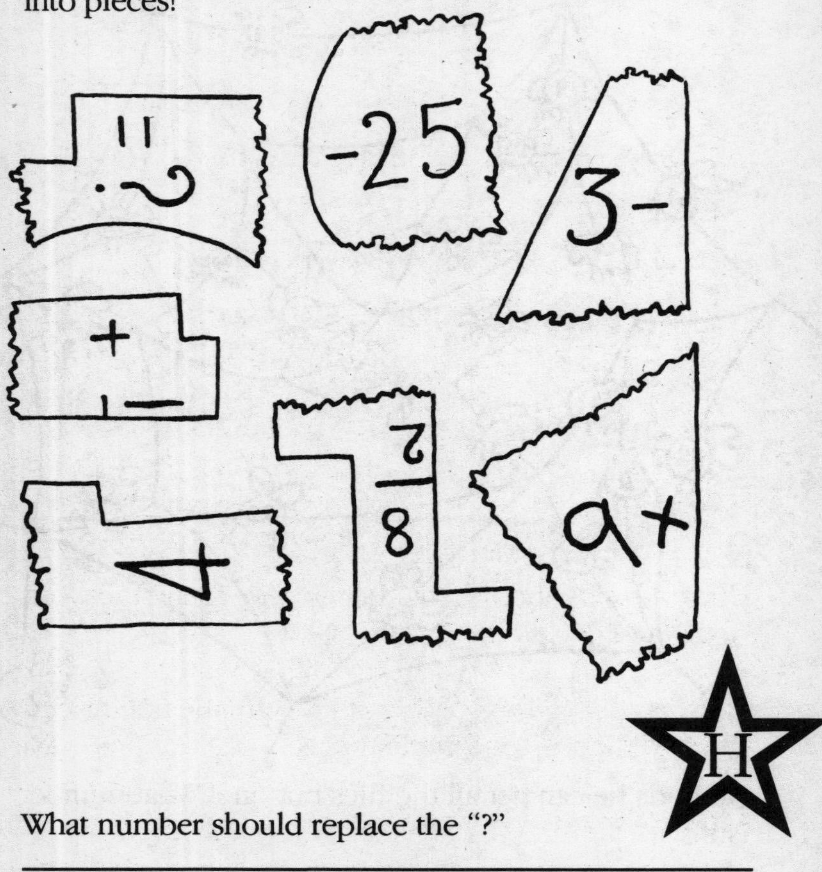

What number should replace the "?"

 ☐ *They never nick themselves.*

Where did the car get a puncture?

Pinned up on the garage wall is this rather boring notice:

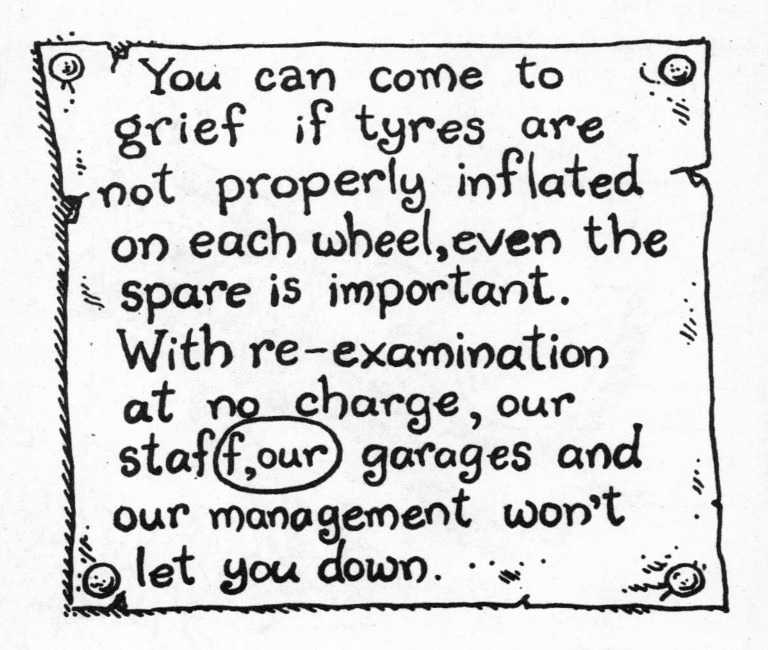

However, somebody has rather cleverly found the word "four" and circled it.

There are five other numbers hidden in the notice. Can you find them all and circle them?

Add up all six circled numbers.

What flies under water?

Our diver, Seymore Fish, is exploring some underwater caves. He wants to get to the octopus, but he must swim through even and odd numbered caves alternately.

Add up the odd numbers he passes and take them away from the sum of the even ones!

 ☐ *Because the bottom is at the top!*

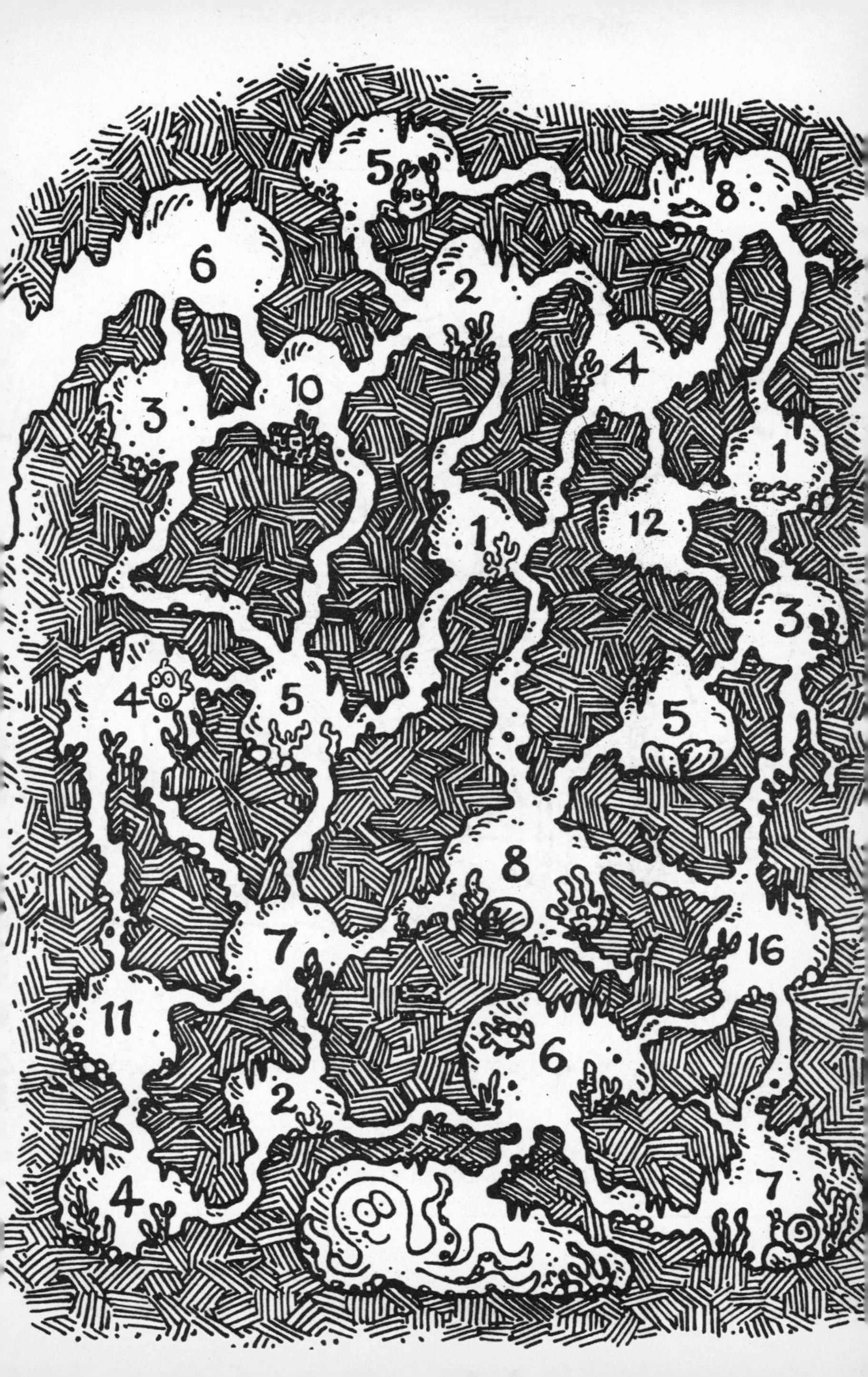
5
8
6
2
10
4
3
1
1
12
3
4
5
5
8
7
16
11
6
2
4
7

How does the sea say hello?

Here's a jolly picture of the seaside with numbers on it.

What colour would you expect each of the numbered objects to be?

Write each colour in its numbered space in the grid.

Which number reads downwards?

A window. □

What did the flower say to his girlfriend?

Here's a very proud gardener, Col. E. Flower. His four favourite plants have all flowered together.

The unusual Tartan Prongstalk only flowers every sixth month.

The Fairy's Sneezewort only flowers in every fourth month.

 ☐ *Under his Buccanhat.*

The Giant Climbing Pizza Plant only flowers every five months.

The vicious worm-eating Gobble Shrub only flowers in every third month.

How many months will it be before they all flower together again?

Butterflies. ☐

HOW ARE YOU GETTING ON?

That's not a joke, it's a question.

If you've solved all the puzzles up to here, then you're about half way to finding THE DEADLIEST JOKE! Well done!

Maybe you think one of the jokes you've already worked out must be the DEADLIEST, but OH NO, IT ISN'T, MATEY!

The DEADLIEST JOKE is deadlier than the man collecting for the old folks home who was given somebody's granny. Yes, it's even deadlier than the baby who's been walking for six months and is halfway to India by now . . .

Could it be more deadly than the man who went big game hunting and shot a twenty foot Monopoly board?

Indeed it is.

 ☐ *They're all redskins.*

SOME HELP

It might help if you trace some of the puzzles out onto bits of paper and then cut them out and shuffle them around until ZAM! the answer becomes obvious. Did you try that for the torn homework on page 42? You could try it for the puzzle on page 31 too, and it might be a good idea for the bathroom tile puzzle coming up on page 59.

By the way, if you were stuck on the CAR BOOT SALE on Page 25, you might be glad to know that Cathy spent 60p on the paint set. You might also be glad to know that Justin Case bought a single Wellington boot because the weather forecast said there'd be one foot of snow.

There's always a double one. ☐

What happens if you put your clock forward every year?

Can you tell the time?

To make it harder, this clock is UPSIDE DOWN and it is being seen in a MIRROR!

Which one of these times does the clock really show?

Work out the correct time and add the four digits together.

A morse toad.

Why won't a barber shave a man with a wooden leg?

Here you see a row of four shops.

The BAKER doesn't live at either end of the row.

The YELLOW door has a higher number than the BUTCHER'S.

The door of Number 64 is GREEN. (In case you're interested, one of the other doors is brown.)

The BICYCLE REPAIR MAN has the shop between the BLUE door and Number 66.

What number is the BARBER'S?

Why did the boy pull the piece of string along the road?

These roads have got rather a lot of holes in them! If each racing car has to stay in his own lane, who will win?

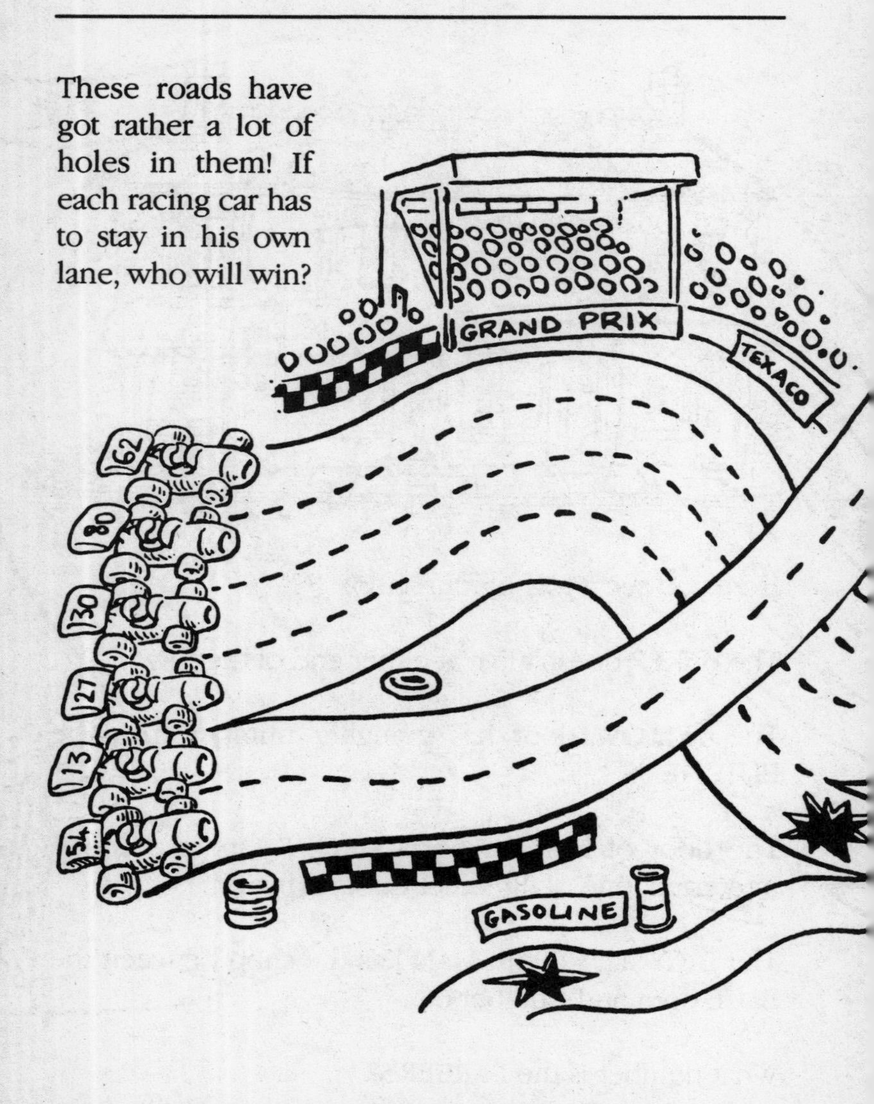

☐ *Newly webs.*

A loony module. ☐

What do you call a map of the desert?

Here's a map of an island with lots of different countries on it. The dotted lines are the borders of all the different countries.

Suppose you have to colour EVERYTHING in!

To start with, the sea and rivers have to be blue. You then have to use other colours to fill in the countries, so that no two countries of the same colour touch each other.

If coloured pencils cost 15p each, what is the smallest amount you'll have to spend?

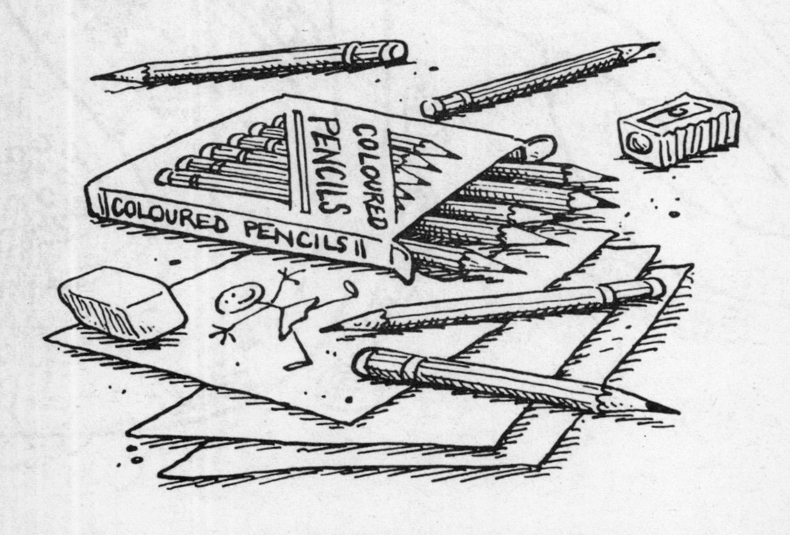

 ☐ *Electric eggs.*

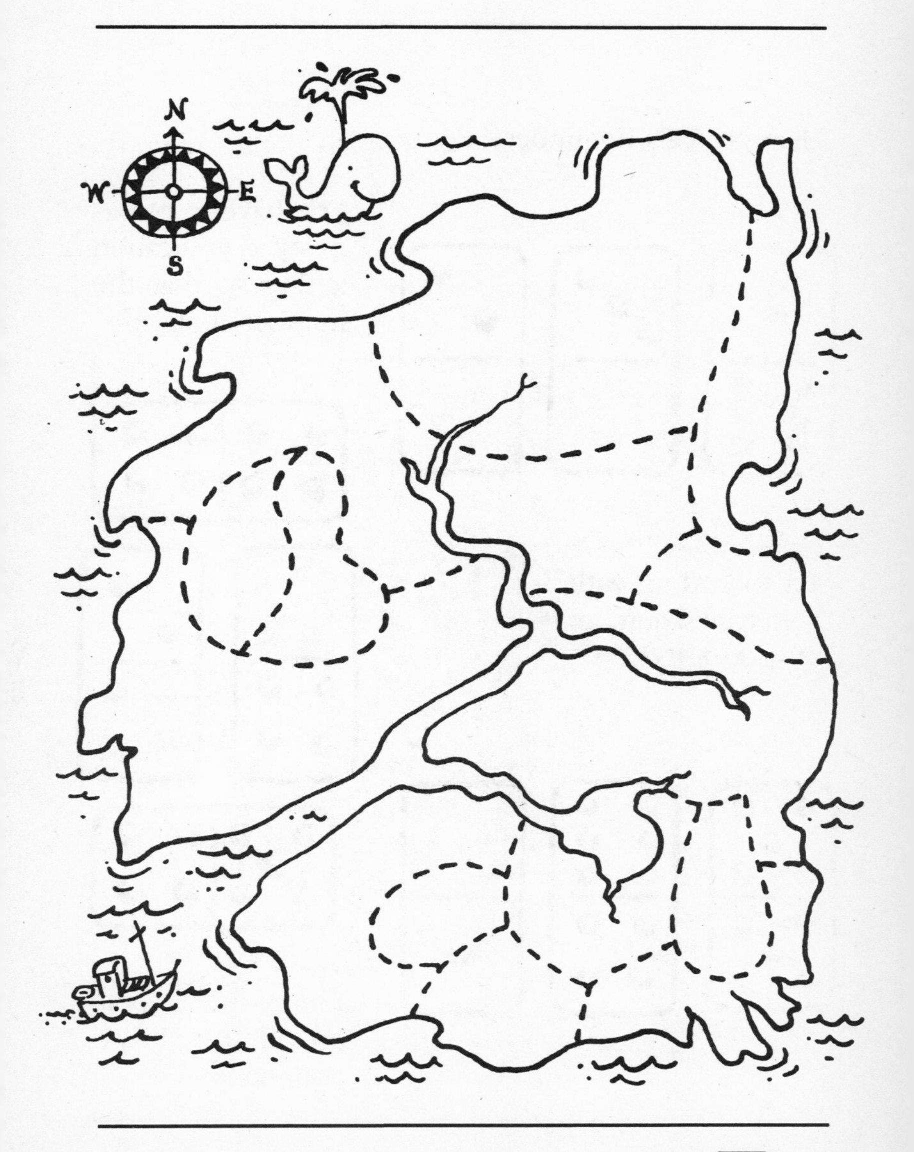

He couldn't control his pupils. ☐

Why does a set of dominoes always have one extra?

Here are TEN dominoes.

You have to put as many as you can in a line so that the numbers link up.

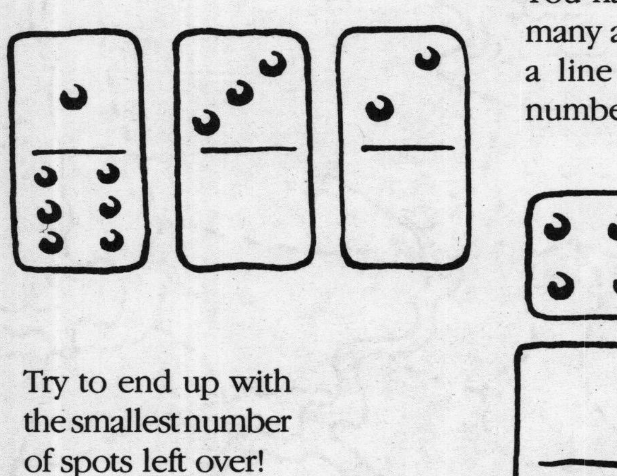

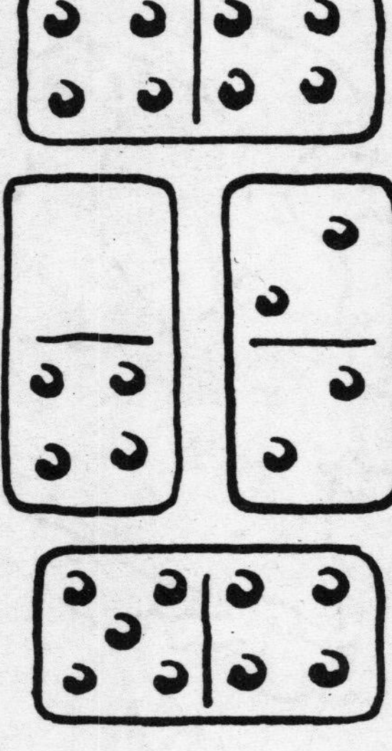

Try to end up with the smallest number of spots left over!

Count up the spots on all the linked dominoes!

 ☐ *The stairs.*

Who always admires you in the shower?

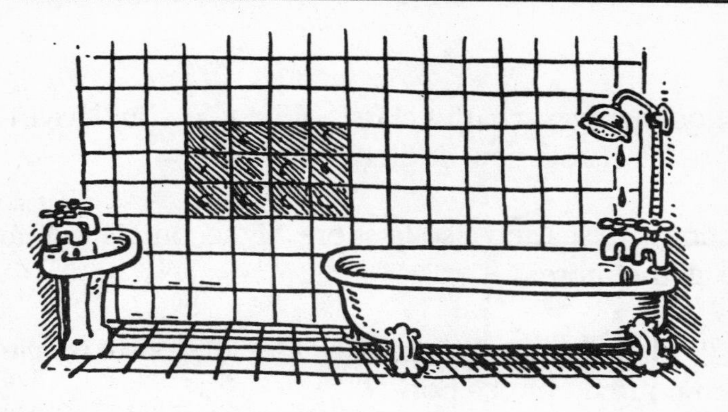

There used to be a big number painted on this bathroom wall, but sadly the tiles have fallen off!

Can you make them into a two figure number?

What has four legs and flies?

To find the answer to this classic old riddle, you'll have to solve this classic new riddle!

My first is in sea and also in shore. My second is so I can see all the more.

My third can be cross, or times by a lot. My fourth is quite often poured out of a pot.

My fifth is a question, all in a letter, my next escapes lock but it's caught up in fetter.

All of the rest describes mine and yours but that's not the end of this riddle because . . .

The number you seek can be caught unawares as a pair of pairs of pairs of pairs of pairs of PAIRS!

Why are prisoners such slow readers?

The librarian, Linda Buckout, was very worried. She had a set of seventeen books, but only sixteen fitted the shelves.

She thought her boss Phil V Temper might tell her off, but she need not have worried. When he saw the shelves, he was so taken with her clever arrangement of books, he forgot about the extra one. Can you see why?

(HINT: add up the book numbers in any row, across, down or diagonally! Or add the four corners . . . or the four in the middle . . .)

Why are policemen such good shavers?

The Police Sergeant, Les B Avinnyoo, has a street plan showing where his constables are.

He has to make sure that at least one policeman can see right down each street.

Suddenly, a man dashes into headquarters, complaining he's had his bottom pinched. Sergeant Les needs to call in three of his men to get it back.

Which three can he call in and still leave his streets fully watched?

Add their numbers.

You're too young to be engaged. ☐

Why did the pilot go to the doctor?

One day, Terry Fickoldchap, the well-known pilot and explorer, was standing in the officer's mess. He suddenly realised and dashed off to clean his shoes but, unfortunately for him, he accidentally dropped this secret air chart.

It was discovered by Elma Wigslipt, the very badly disguised spy.

Elma knew one of the numbers on the chart was a TOP SECRET number, but did not know which one!

☐ *Two pairs of trousers.*

In fact, if you examine the chart, only one of the numbers is in the right place!

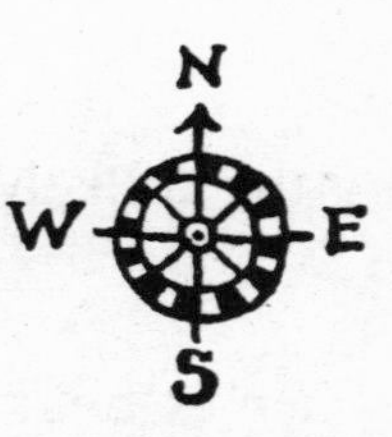

S	W	N	S	W	17	E	89
W	63	86	81	S	N	40	N
E	79	W	23	64	E	24	E
W	42	29	N	W	78	N	16
52	N	33	49	E	70	90	43
W	19	S	44	12	62	36	S
S	22	75	S	55	18	S	E
E	69	W	83	46	72	22	E
N	S	15	48	87	S	61	W
W	31	E	39	S	N	E	N

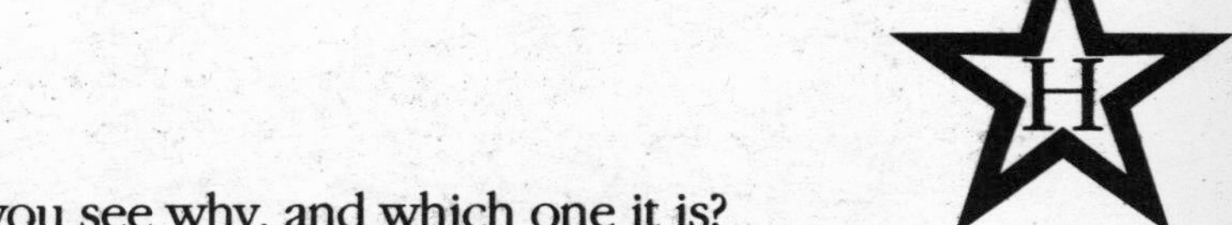

Can you see why, and which one it is?

Why did the window cleaner's bucket look sick?

This is the unlikely but true story of the window cleaner's race.

The race is held outside the offices of Trans World International Telecommunication Services, where a large scaffolding arrangement has been raised.

Out of one hundred competitors, only five window cleaners have reached the grand final. They are numbers 28, 34, 53, 82 and 87. Their starting positions are marked on the plan opposite.

The object is to be the first window cleaner to reach the bucket.

The window cleaners can walk along a plank TWICE as fast as they can climb UP a ladder, but only HALF as fast as they can climb DOWN a ladder!

Assuming they can all go at exactly the same speed . . .

 ☐ *It's easier with a razor.*

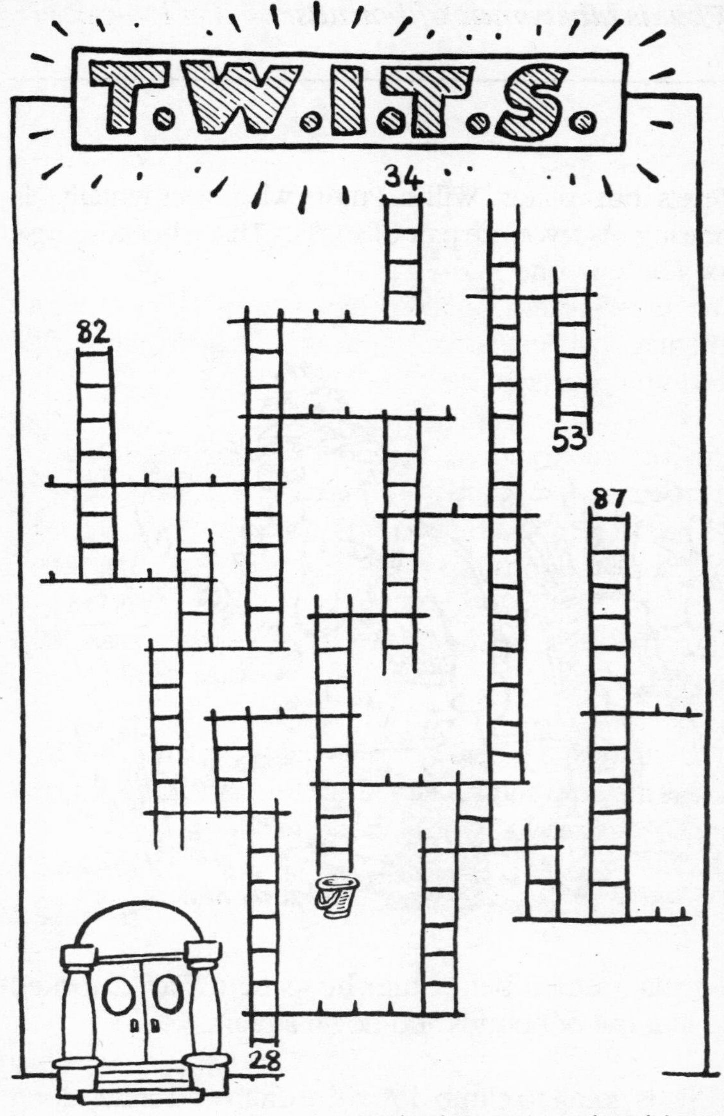

Which number should win?

What is always out of bounds?

Here's our golfer, Willie Puttit, who, incidentally, is wearing his favourite pair of socks. (That's because he's got a hole in one.)

Like many others before him, he seems to have knocked his ball out of bounds and down a drain.

Willie is going to climb down the drain and crawl along until he reaches the outlet.

 ☐ *Because of the sand which is there.*

If he picks up every single ball he passes, what is the *smallest* number of golf balls he can come out with?

What's big and wobbly in Paris?

Four people who used to be friends went to a posh restaurant in Paris. They each ordered one item.

The bill came to 210 Francs, and naturally they all argued over how much everybody should pay.

Madge argued with Bill because his snailburger (with slime relish) cost twice as much as her pommes frites, which incidentally is French for French fries, which is American for chips.

Bill then turned to Ethel and said her frog pie had cost the same as his snailburger and Madge's chips put together.

Ethel defended herself by saying that if Fred had had frog pie instead of champagne, the bill would only have been 180 Francs.

Needless to say, by this time, Fred had sneaked away. How much did the others have to pay for his champagne?

At the fork in the road. ☐

What noise does a squashed grape make?

Try to find these numbers squashed in the grid!

1 · 2 · 3 · 5 · 6 · 7 · 8 · 10

11 · 12 · 13 · 15 · 20 · 30 · 50 · 90

You also need to find these words:

LOW HIGH DOZEN ZERO

The words can appear written in any direction: up, down, backwards, forwards, diagonally, vertically, horizontally, skilfully, neatly, happily. . .

Put a line through each word as you find it.

Circle any letters left over in the grid.

 ☐ *He had flu in his plane.*

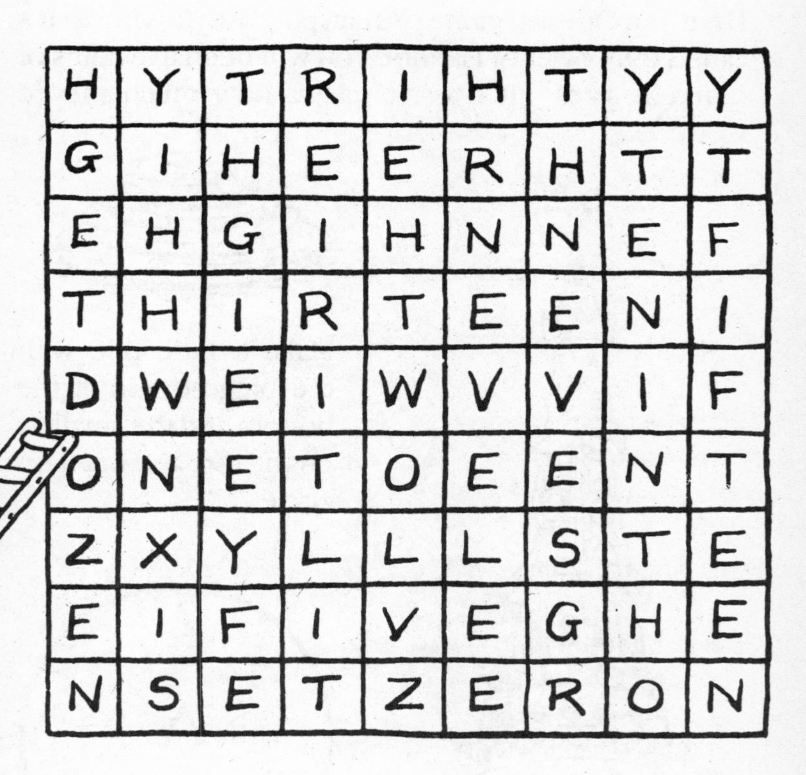

Use the letters you circled to make another number.

What flavour is an Arab's favourite packet of crisps?

Here's an Oriental game you can play with this book! It's called the Tower of Hannoi. You will need five coins of different sizes. (It doesn't matter how much they're worth.)

Make a little pile with the biggest coin at the bottom and the smallest on the top, and put it on circle "A".

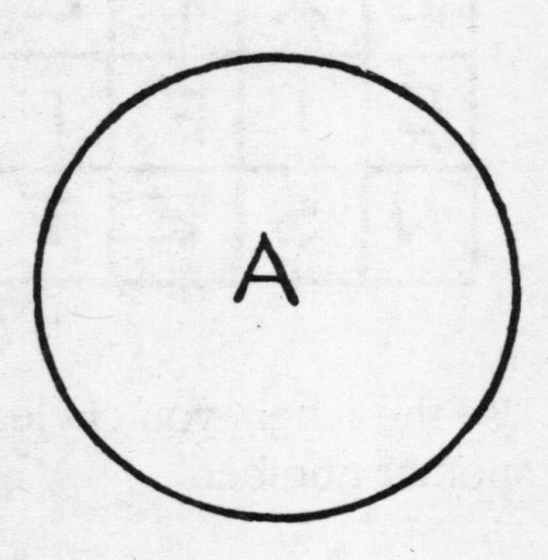

 ☐ *The bathroom fan.*

What you have to do is move the coins about between the three circles until the whole pile is on circle "B"!

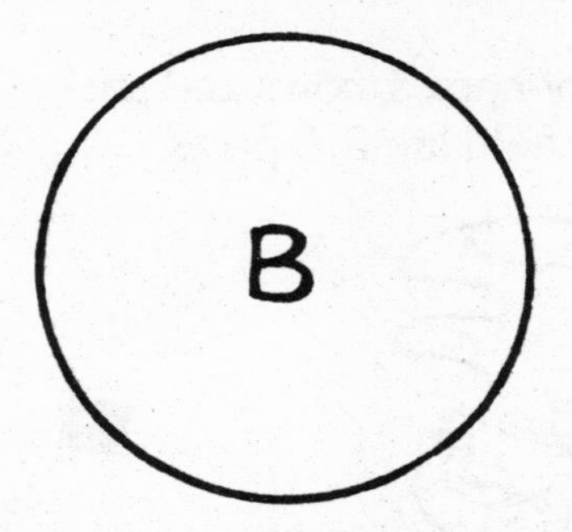

You can only move one coin at a time.

You must never put a bigger coin on top of a smaller coin.

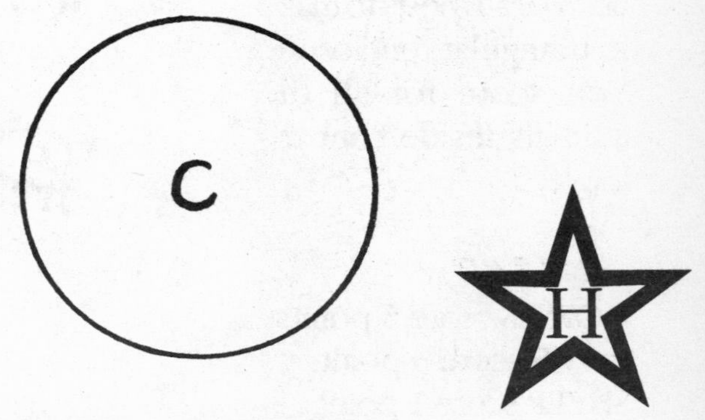

What's the smallest number of moves you need?

Sandpaper. ☐

Why don't tomatoes make very good cowboys?

Here's a good ol' cowboy game!

A field is full of horses, cows and sheep. Planted in the field are five posts.

You have a long rope which you can tie around any THREE posts to make a triangular enclosure. You score for all the animals inside your triangle.

HORSES score 5 points
COWS score 3 points
SHEEP score 1 point . . .
. . what's the best you can score?

Dates. ☐

Why did the man have trouble getting his granny on the train?

____

This train cannot reverse or double back on points. Which is the only depot it can reach?

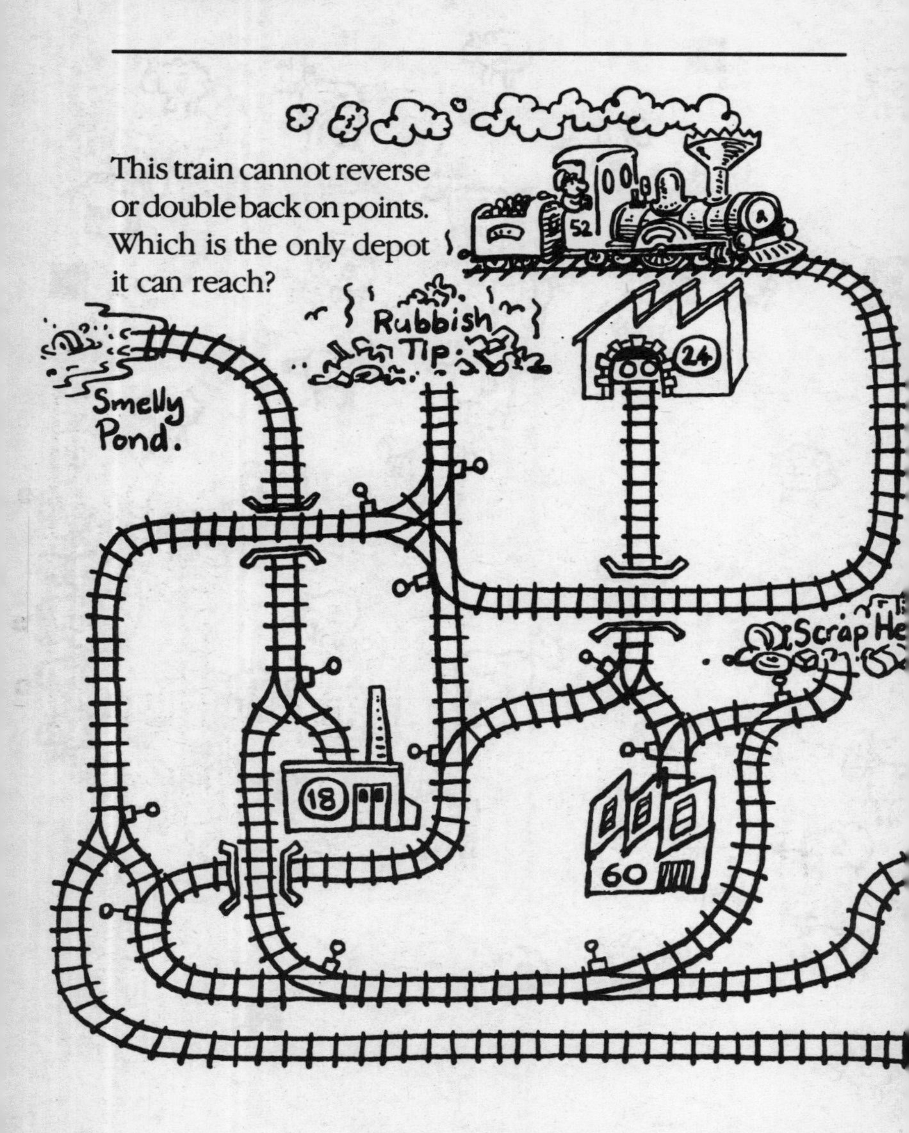

____

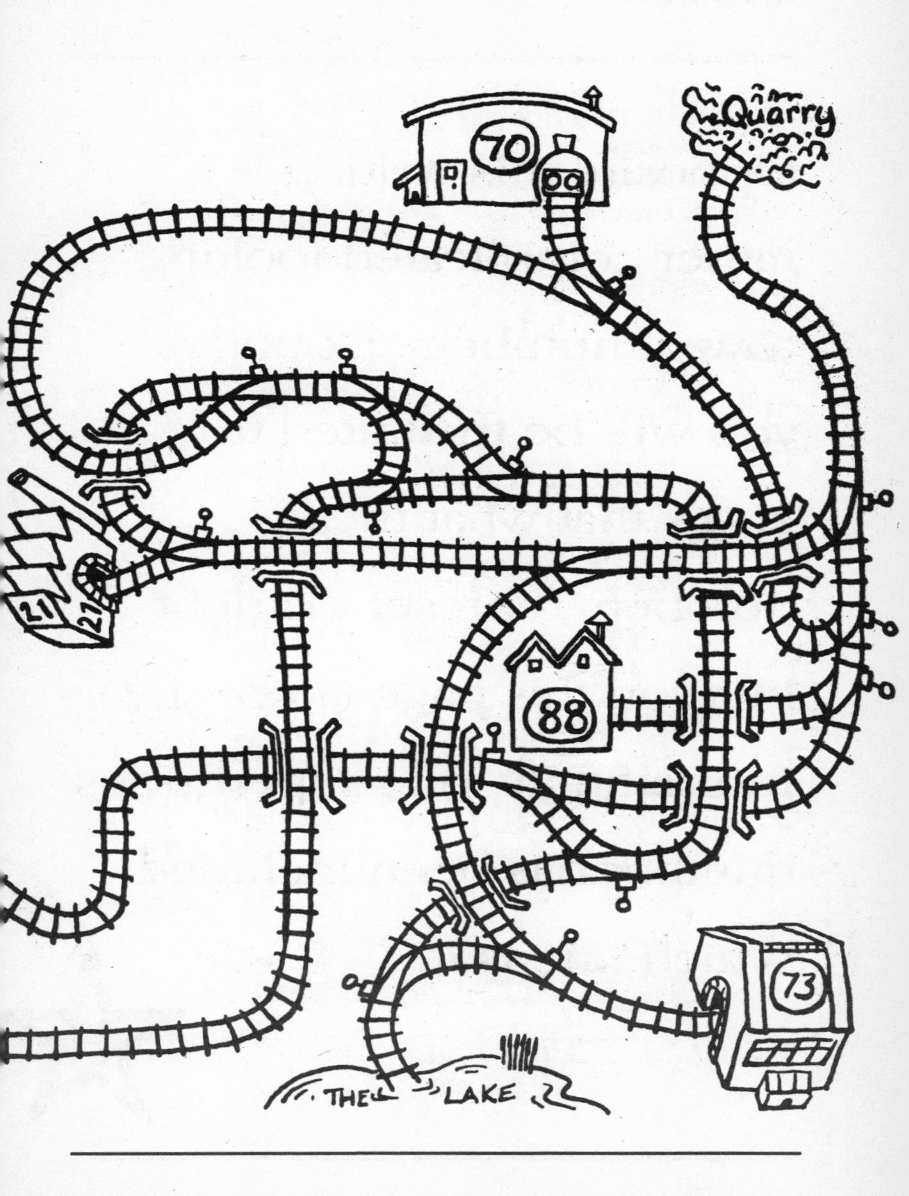
70
Quarry
21
21
88
73
THE LAKE

Opposite this writing is a rather complicated-looking row of numbers. Doubtless you will be frustrated to know that what these numbers represent is right here on this page (honestly). Infuriatingly, one superfluous number has been included. Which one is it?

H

He couldn't push it.

8 4 7 2 10 ONE
6 11 VII
3 2 7 9
3 4 2 X 2
4 4 5
7 9 2 5
4 II 4 4 8
13 three 11
6 5 IV 8
3 2 2

Why did the bull rush?

These bulrushes are growing by a village pond, which has an arrangement of stepping stones, some of which are numbered.

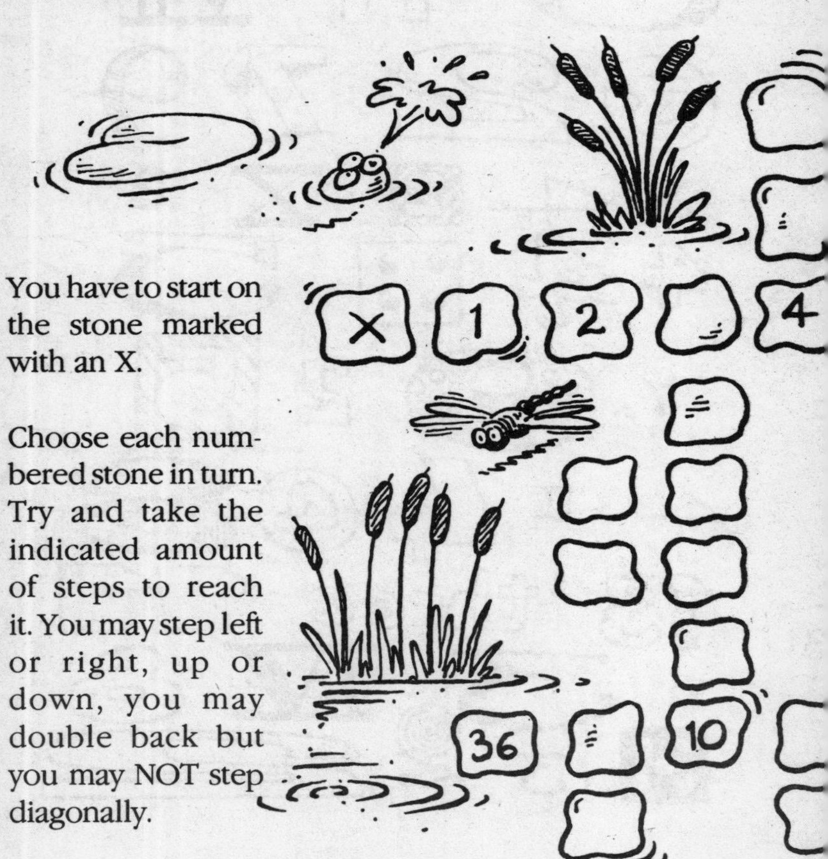

You have to start on the stone marked with an X.

Choose each numbered stone in turn. Try and take the indicated amount of steps to reach it. You may step left or right, up or down, you may double back but you may NOT step diagonally.

 ☐ *He won by six laps.*

This is possible, for all the numbered stones . . . except one! Which one is it?

Why isn't a fortnight very strong?

You'll have noticed by now that quite a lot of people in this book have birthdays and Wes Meepresent is no exception.

Everybody in his family has a birthday in May. A few years ago, on Sunday May 15th, his good-looking, clever, handsome, brilliant elder brother, Kjartan, was having his birthday.

His mum's birthday was the Friday after that.
His sister Agnes's birthday was exactly two weeks before his mum's.
His dad's came on the Thursday after Agnes's.
If you reversed the date of Dad's birthday, you got Granny's birthday.

Wes's birthday was the second Monday after Granny's, so what number was the day of the month that Wes was born on?

A FEW EXTRA HINTS:

It's now page 85. Have the silly dice on page 18 been bothering you? Yes? In that case you've had 67 pages of being bothered. (Tee hee hee.) Never mind – it'll be worth it when you decode the DEADLIEST JOKE!

Treat yourself to some fun! What you need is a pencil and two square things such as two sugar cubes. Deal with the dice on the left hand side first. Copy the numbers you can see onto one sugar cube . . . you must make sure you get the numbers the same way up as they appear on page 18. You should be able to fill in all six sides from the three pictures. Do the same for the right hand dice. You can then solve the puzzle!

For the tower of Hannoi, on page 74, first of all, try the puzzle with just two different coins. It should take you three moves . . . easy peasy! Now try with three coins, that should take seven moves. Four coins will take you fifteen moves . . . O.K? Now try five coins again!

Fryer Tuck. ☐

What did the big telephone say to the little telephone?

This is, of course, a very old telephone joke, so here's an interesting fact about old-fashioned telephones. They used to have dials that you had to put your finger in and turn round.

Next to the numbers there were letters, like this:

A secret code was based on this! Suppose you wanted to say HELLO in code, you would dial: 4, 3, 5, 5, 6. This number can be translated as HELLO!

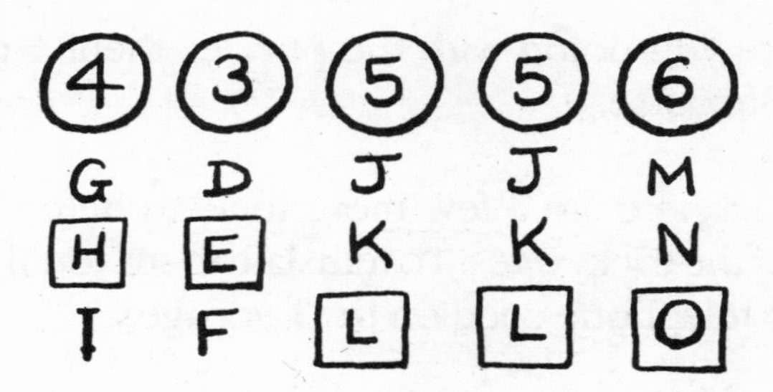

It can also be translated as GFKJM which means nothing, so you have to choose the words which make sense!

You guessed it, to get the number you want, for this answer you'll have to work out what number was spelt out when somebody dialled this.

in a brick. ☐

EVEN MORE HINTS!

How are you doing with the puzzles then? Easy? Too easy? Of course.

However, here are a few more hints to help you with some of the tricky ones. To translate them you'll need to use the telephone code on the last page.

The complicated numbers on page 81 . . . either you saw it immediately or you didn't! If you didn't, then look at the message and:

Remember the cog wheels in the first puzzle? None of the arrows should end up pointing at a number

For the squashed numbers on page 73, you should have:

(3)(5)(3)(8)(3)(6) letters left over.

The bathroom tiles on page 59 make up a two-digit number. The digits are:

(7)(3)(8)(3)(6) and (3)(6)(8)(7)

Finally the air map on page 65 . . . get a mirror and read this:

ONLY ONE NUMBER HAS AN
"N" DIRECTLY TO THE
NORTH, AN "S" DIRECTLY
TO THE SOUTH, AN "E" TO
THE EAST AND A "W"
TO THE WEST!

What shoes do railway engines wear?

Welcome to GNOME RAIL!

Gnomes don't have roads. Instead, they drive little railway engines along tracks going to their houses.

Here is a map showing a bit of the track leading to five houses. The arrows show which way the points are going to start with.

Gnomes HATE being followed, so whenever a Gnome goes over a point, he quickly changes the point to make the next train go the other way!

What number house does the sixth Gnome get to?

____

YOU'RE NEARLY THERE!

Well, you are if you've solved ALL the puzzles in the book. Have you? And have you ticked off ALL the answers?

In that case, if you check through the book, you will find FOUR answers that are unticked. This is because they are not answers at all but a SECRET CODE!

WHAT YOU DO NOW

1 Turn the page. Do you see the grids? Good.

2 Turn the page back and read this:

3 You must write the unticked answers in GRID A exactly in the order that you found them, starting with the one nearest the front of the book. You have to put one letter in each square, and miss out any spaces between words. When you finish writing out one answer, start straight away with the next one.

4 When you finish, you should have exactly one letter in every square. If you haven't, . . . oh dear! You'll have to start the WHOLE BOOK all over again!

5 When GRID A is ready, turn TWO pages . . . (exciting isn't it?)

CODE GRID A

[ ]	[ ]	[ ]	[ ]	[ ]	[ ]	[ ]
1	2	3	4	5	6	7
[ ]	[ ]	[ ]	[ ]	[ ]	[ ]	[ ]
8	9	10	11	12	13	14
[ ]	[ ]	[ ]	[ ]	[ ]	[ ]	[ ]
15	16	17	18	19	20	21
[ ]	[ ]	[ ]	[ ]	[ ]	[ ]	[ ]
22	23	24	25	26	27	28
[ ]	[ ]	[ ]	[ ]	[ ]	[ ]	[ ]
29	30	31	32	33	34	35
[ ]	[ ]	[ ]	[ ]	[ ]	[ ]	[ ]
36	37	38	39	40	41	42
[ ]	[ ]	[ ]	[ ]	[ ]	[ ]	[ ]
43	44	45	46	47	48	49
[ ]	[ ]	[ ]	[ ]	[ ]	[ ]	[ ]
50	51	52	53	54	55	56
[ ]	[ ]	[ ]	[ ]	[ ]	[ ]	[ ]
57	58	59	60	61	62	63
[ ]	[ ]	[ ]	[ ]	[ ]	[ ]	[ ]
64	65	66	67	68	69	70
[ ]	[ ]	[ ]	[ ]	[ ]	[ ]	
71	72	73	74	75	76	

Now just copy each letter from GRID A to

CODE GRID B

[ ]	[ ]	[ ]	[ ]	[ ]	[ ]	[ ]
72	31	51	66	68	59	12
[ ]	[ ]	[ ]	[ ]	[ ]	[ ]	[ ]
53	75	24	65	7	11	70
[ ]	[ ]	[ ]	[?]	[ ]	[ ]	[ ]
26	37	22	?	57	56	43
[ ]	[ ]	[ ]	[ ]	[ ]	[ ]	[ ]
69	29	28	23	74	76	49
[ ]	[ ]	[ ]	[ ]	[ ]	[ ]	[ ]
44	71	6	34	9	6	61
[ ]	[ ]	[ ]	[ ]	[ ]	[ ]	[ ]
50	56	73	22	42	47	72
[ ]	[ ]	[ ]	[ ]	[ ]	[ ]	[ ]
17	33	70	3	3	15	32
[ ]	[ ]	[ ]	[ ]	[ ]	[ ]	[ ]
35	8	27	2	63	55	8
[ ]	[ ]	[ ]	[ ]	[ ]	[ ]	[ ]
9	59	49	47	50	13	45
[ ]	[ ]	[ ]	[ ]	[ ]	[ ]	[ ]
61	15	1	58	64	16	5
[ ]	[ ]	[ ]	[ ]	[ ]	[ ]	[ ]
40	54	63	25	39	38	30
[ ]	[ ]	[ ]	[ ]	[ ]	[ ]	[ ]
20	10	45	14	36	60	46

wherever its number appears in GRID B!

THE JOKE HAS NOW APPEARED IN GRID B!

THERE! What do you think eh?

Isn't that terrible? Yet somehow magnificent at the same time? Be honest, wasn't it worth all the effort?
. . . of course you DID realise that you have to read the joke from the bottom left hand corner upwards, then read the next column upwards and so on . . . didn't you?

FINAL CAUTION

At the wrong place, to the wrong person at the wrong time, this joke could prove

FATAL!